THE PHILANTHROPIST

a bourgeois comedy

by

Christopher Hampton

C'est que jamais, morbleu! les hommes n'ont raison
MOLIERE, *"Le Misanthrope"*

FABER AND FABER
London

822
HAM

First published in 1970
by Faber and Faber Limited
24 Russell Square London WC1
Printed in Great Britain by
Latimer Trend & Co Ltd Plymouth

ISBN (paper edition) 0 571 09527 5
ISBN (cloth edition) 0 571 09520 8

FOR LAURA

The Philanthropist opened at the Royal Court Theatre, London, in July 1970 with Alec McCowen as Philip and Jane Asher as Celia, directed by Robert Kidd, designed by John Gunter.

CHARACTERS

PHILIP
DONALD
JOHN
CELIA
BRAHAM
ELIZABETH
ARAMINTA

The play is set in the near future,
and its characters are aged between 23 and 35

ONE

PHILIP'S *room. The room of a bachelor don, comfortable but not well-furnished, ordered but not tidy.* PHILIP *and* DONALD *sit relaxed but attentive, one in an armchair, one on the sofa perhaps.* JOHN, *a younger man, is sitting in a wooden chair, a pile of papers on his knee. He holds a revolver.*

JOHN: You needn't think I'm not serious. Because I am. I assure you I am. Can't you see that? I've come here this evening because I think both of you are responsible for this and I think you deserve it as much as I do. If you hate me for doing it, that's your problem. It won't concern me. I just want you to have one vivid image of me, that's all, one memory to last all your life and never vanish, to remind you that if you won, I lost, and that nobody can win without somebody losing. Good-bye. (*He puts the revolver to his head.*) Bang. (*He smiles uneasily at them.*) Curtain.
(*Silence.*)
Do you like it?
PHILIP: Very good. Would you like another drink?
JOHN: Oh, yes, thanks, er . . . Philip.
(PHILIP *pours a drink.*)
PHILIP: Ice?
JOHN: Please.
(*Exit* PHILIP.)
JOHN: He doesn't like it, does he?
DON: Oh, I don't know.
JOHN: He doesn't. I can tell.
DON: I'm sure he does like it.

JOHN: Do you?

(PHILIP *returns with the ice.*)

DON: Well. Yes and no. I mean there are some enormously promising things in the play. Obviously it's basically a conversation piece, but you do try to give the customers a bit of everything—a touch of melodrama, the odd *coup de théâtre*, humour, tragedy, monologues and pastoral inter-ludes, yes, yes, I like that, generous. But on the other hand I think there are certain . . . lapses, which, you know, detract from the play as a satisfying whole.

JOHN: You mean it's stylistically heterogeneous?

PHILIP: I think Don prefers to see it as an unsatisfying whole. (*He laughs merrily and alone.*) Sorry. Would you like a chocolate?

JOHN: No, thanks.

PHILIP: Don? I think I'll have one.

(*He helps himself to one, as he is to throughout this scene.*)

JOHN: Tell me what you don't like about it.

DON: Well, one thing is that character who appears every so often with a ladder. The window-cleaner. What's his name?

JOHN: Man.

DON: Yes. Well, I take it he has some kind of allegorical significance outside the framework of the play. I mean I don't know if this is right but I rather took him to signify England.

JOHN: No, no, erm, in point of fact he signifies man.

DON: Ah.

JOHN: Yes.

DON: Hence the name.

JOHN: Yes.

DON: I see.

JOHN: Although now you come to mention it, I suppose he could be taken to represent England.

PHILIP: Is that two ns?

JOHN: What?

PHILIP: In Man.

JOHN: No, one.

PHILIP: Ah, well, you see, I thought it was two ns. As in Thomas.

JOHN: Thomas?

PHILIP: Thomas Mann.

JOHN: Oh.

PHILIP: So I thought he was just meant to represent a window-cleaner.

JOHN: Well . . .

PHILIP: Under the circumstances, I think you've integrated him into the plot very well.

JOHN: Thank you. (*He seems displeased.*)

DON: I always think the beginning and the end are the most difficult parts of a play to handle, and I'm not sure you've been entirely successful with either.

JOHN: Aren't you?

DON: I can't really say I like that Pirandello-style beginning. It's been done so often, you know. I mean I'm not saying that your use of it isn't resourceful. It is. But the device itself is a bit rusty.

JOHN: Yes, perhaps you're right. I'm not really very happy about the beginning myself. (*To* PHILIP.) What do you think?

PHILIP: I liked it.

JOHN: Why?

PHILIP: No special reason, I just liked it. You shouldn't take any notice of me, though, I'm not really qualified to comment.

JOHN: You do lecture in English, don't you?

PHILIP: Yes, but in philology, not literature.

JOHN: Philology? Don't you find that incredibly tedious?

PHILIP: No, it's exactly the right subject for me. I'm fascinated by words.

JOHN: Individual rather than consecutive.

PHILIP: Yes. My only advice to writers is "make the real shapes".

JOHN: Pardon?

11

PHILIP: It's an anagram of "Shakespeare" and "Hamlet".

DON: He's obsessed by anagrams.

JOHN (*coldly*): Really. (*Pause.*) What's your objection to the end of the play?

DON: It just doesn't convince me. It seems artificial. Do you really think he'd commit suicide in front of them like that?

JOHN: Yes. Why not?

DON: It doesn't seem to tie in with his character as we've seen it in the rest of the play.

PHILIP: I don't know. I liked it.

JOHN: You don't have to say that, you know. I'd much prefer to have honest criticism than your, if you don't mind me saying so, rather negative remarks.

PHILIP: Please take no notice of what I say. I always like things. I get pleasure from the words that are used, whatever the subject is. I've enjoyed every book I've ever read for one reason or another. That's why I can't teach literature. I have no critical faculties. I think there's always something good to be found in the product of another man's mind. Even if the man is, by all objective standards, a complete fool. So you see I'd like a play however terrible it was.

JOHN: So you think my play is terrible.

PHILIP: I didn't say that, I . . .

JOHN: I'm not an idiot, you know, I can take a hint.

PHILIP: Please don't get angry.

JOHN (*furious*): I am not angry! I just don't think there's any point in our discussing it any more, that's all. It's different with Don, Don has some constructive criticisms to make, which will probably be very helpful.

PHILIP: But I like the play more than Don does, I think it's very good.

JOHN: There's no need to be hypocritical.

PHILIP: I . . .

JOHN: I have no illusions about this play, you know. . . .

PHILIP: I . . .

JOHN: But I do think it has a little more merit than you give it

12

credit for.

PHILIP: I'm sorry.

JOHN: Never mind.

(*Silence.*)

PHILIP: Would you like a chocolate?

JOHN: No.

(*Silence.*)

JOHN (*to* DON): Now, what were you saying?

DON: I was just wondering whether the suicide is altogether justified.

JOHN: Oh, I think so. Given the kind of man he is. I think it could be quite powerful. I think perhaps he might put the revolver in his mouth. Then, if the back wall of the set was whitewashed, they could use some quaint device to cover it with great gobs of brain and bright blood at the vital moment. And just the two of them sitting there gaping. That would be wonderful.

(*To illustrate,* JOHN *puts the revolver into his mouth and presses the trigger. Loud explosion. By some quaint device, gobs of brain and bright blood appear on the whitewashed wall.* PHILIP *and* DON *sit gaping. Long silence.*)

DON: Jesus.

(JOHN *slumps to the ground.* PHILIP *rushes abruptly from the stage.* DON *gropes shakily for the telephone and begins to dial.*)

BLACKOUT
(*The first movement of the 2nd Brandenburg Concerto*)

TWO

A few days later. PHILIP *alone, laying the dinner-table for six. A knock at the door.* DON *enters.*

DON: Hello. Am I too early?

PHILIP: No.

DON: I wondered if there was anything I could do to help.

PHILIP: No, it's all under control. Help yourself to a drink.

(DON *pours himself a Scotch.*)

DON: For you?

PHILIP: No, thanks. Not just yet.

(DON *sits down.*)

DON: Where's Celia?

PHILIP: In the kitchen.

DON: Are you all right?

PHILIP: Yes. Why?

DON: I don't know, you seem a little morose.

PHILIP: I am a bit.

DON: Why? You're not still upset about John, are you?

PHILIP: Well . . .

DON: I can't think why. You hardly knew the man.

PHILIP: That doesn't make any difference.

DON: Well, it should do. He was my friend, not yours. And I haven't been sitting around brooding about it for days. You're too sensitive, Philip, really. I mean, the whole thing was just a grotesque accident.

PHILIP: I've never seen anyone dead before. I've never seen anyone die.

DON: I don't know, the whole evening was a complete disaster.

14

I mean, apart from that. I only suggested we had it here because I knew I'd hate the play, and I wanted someone around who'd say something nice to him. I don't know why he got so ratty with you.

PHILIP: Well, I was very tactless.

DON: Nonsense, he was absurd. A sad case in many ways. There's no doubt he was very intelligent, but he had no idea how to write. That play was no good at all.

PHILIP: I rather liked it.

DON: I know you did, but it was no good. The ideas were there, but not the technique, it was far too cerebral.

PHILIP: Under the circumstances, I think that's an uniquely unfortunate adjective.

DON: What? Oh, oh yes. (*He laughs.*) Anyway, I see you've managed to get him off the wall.

PHILIP: Don.

DON: Sorry.

(*Silence.*)

PHILIP: Celia wasn't very sympathetic either. The first thing she said when I rang her up and told her about it was: "I'm not surprised, he's always been ludicrously absent-minded."

DON: Did she?

PHILIP: Yes.

DON: Come to think of it, absent-minded's even more unfortunate than cerebral. (*He laughs, recovers, shakes his head.*) No, it was a terrible thing to happen, really. (*He tries to look solemn, but is suddenly overcome by helpless laughter.*) Sorry. (CELIA *enters.*)

CELIA: What's the joke?

DON: John.

(*She puts some mats on the table.*)

CELIA: It's all very well for you to laugh, you didn't have to clean him up. He was all over the place.

PHILIP: Please, love . . .

CELIA: Philip had to throw away his Picasso print, didn't you? (*She heads for the door.*)

PHILIP: Can I do anything in the kitchen?

CELIA: I've yet to see any evidence of it.

(CELIA *goes out*.)

DON: Who's coming this evening?

PHILIP: Liz.

DON: Good.

PHILIP: Erm . . . Araminta, do you know her?

DON: Oh, really, where did you pick her up?

PHILIP: I didn't pick her up. She's one of the few people I come into contact with who has any interest in my subject at all. She seems quite intelligent, so I asked her.

DON: I don't think it's your subject she's interested in.

PHILIP: Oh?

DON: Haven't you heard about her?

PHILIP: No.

DON: The quickest drawers in the faculty. Old Noakes was telling me the other day he literally had to beg her to leave him in peace.

PHILIP: Did he really?

DON: Yes. So I should keep your hand on your ha'penny if I were you. (*Pause*.) Who else?

PHILIP: Braham Head.

DON: The novelist?

PHILIP: Yes. He's up here for a couple of weeks. Celia met him at some party and wanted to ask him. Do you know him?

DON: Slightly.

PHILIP: What's he like?

DON: Incredible prick. He's one of those writers who've been forced to abandon the left-wing for tax reasons.

PHILIP: I quite like one or two of his books.

DON: They're dreadful. Dreadful. The man hasn't a glimmer of talent. And he's so rude and loud.

PHILIP: Oh.

DON: He left his wife last year. He said to her: "Darling, I hope you're not going to be bourgeois about this, but I'm going to leave you and the children for a few months."

16

PHILIP: What happened?

DON: She divorced him. Best thing she could have done. Their whole relationship was soured by her failure even to attempt suicide, which he apparently regarded as unforgivable. He likes to think of himself as a Romantic.

PHILIP: Surely he's not that bad?

DON: Worse. Worse. (*He broods for a moment.*) What about the Prime Minister, then?

PHILIP: What about him?

DON: Haven't you heard?

PHILIP: No.

DON: He's been killed.

PHILIP: What?

DON: Assassinated.

PHILIP: Has he?

DON: They've had nothing else on the radio all day.

PHILIP: How terrible.

DON: Most of the Cabinet as well.

PHILIP: Killed as well?

DON: Yes.

PHILIP: How did it happen?

DON: Well, shortly after the debate began today this rather comic figure came bowling into the courtyard of the House of Commons on a bicycle: an elderly and rather corpulent woman wearing one of those enormous tweed capes, you know, ankle-length. She parked her bicycle, dropped the front wheel into one of those slots they have, and puffed up to the gallery, where she sat for a bit, beaming amiably and sucking Glacier mints. Then, all of a sudden, she leapt to her feet, produced a sub-machine-gun out of nowhere, and mowed down the front bench.

PHILIP: My God.

DON: Yes.

PHILIP: But . . . who was she?

DON: A retired lieutenant-colonel.

PHILIP: Salvation Army?

DON: No, no, she was a man. He gave himself up afterwards. He's completely round the twist. He says he did it to save Britain from the menace of creeping socialism. Says he felt called to be his country's liberator. Apparently he's been practising in his garden in Hampshire for months.

PHILIP: God.

DON: Nine of them he got, and several others wounded. The only one he seemed to be concerned about was the Shadow Minister of Health who was hit in the ankle by a ricochet. He kept saying he hoped he was being treated privately. Then he sauntered off to the cells whistling the Dam Busters' March.

PHILIP: But . . . what's going to happen?

DON: Oh, I don't know, coalition government, another election, something like that. It's not going to make much difference, whatever happens.

PHILIP: Isn't it?

DON: Not to us, anyway.

PHILIP: But . . . it's appalling.

DON: Yes. (*Pause.*) Worse things have happened. (*Pause.*) I must say, I think it was rather boring of him to do it on November the 5th. I suppose in the Tory Party that's the kind of thing that passes for aesthetics.
   (CELIA *enters.*)

CELIA: Did you put the lemons in the 'fridge? I can't see them anywhere.

PHILIP: Oh, God.

CELIA: Don't say you've forgotten them. Honestly, I ask you to get one thing . . .

PHILIP: I'm sorry. I'll go and get them now.

CELIA: Everything's shut. We shall just have to have it without lemon, that's all.

DON: I think I've got a couple of lemons.

CELIA: Have you?

DON: Yes, in my rooms, in the fruit bowl, I think.

CELIA: Can I nip over and get them?

18

DON: Yes, sure.

CELIA: Thanks.

(*She moves over to the door.*)

PHILIP: Celia.

CELIA: Yes.

PHILIP: Anything I can do to help?

CELIA: No.

(CELIA *goes out.* PHILIP *looks unhappy.*)

DON: When is it you're getting married?

PHILIP: I, er, not sure really. Probably sometime in the vacation.

DON: Are you looking forward to it?

PHILIP: Well, yes, I think so. Why?

DON: Just wondered.

(*Silence.*)

PHILIP: You don't really think it's a good idea, do you?

DON: I don't know, Philip.

PHILIP: I mean, you don't really like her, do you?

DON: It's not that I don't like her, that's not it at all. She's very amusing and intelligent and attractive—it's just I sometimes wonder whether she's your kind of person.

PHILIP: What do you mean? You mean I'm not amusing and intelligent and attractive.

DON: Of course not. But you're rather . . . serious, aren't you?

PHILIP: I suppose so.

DON: And Celia isn't. In fact, she's rather frivolous.

PHILIP: But I like that.

DON: Oh, I'm sure you do. Sure you do. But it may cause you some trouble.

PHILIP: She is very malicious sometimes. She does seem to hate a large number of people I find perfectly harmless. Intensely. At first, I didn't think she really hated them, but I'm not so sure now.

DON: Have you ever thought about Liz?

PHILIP: Liz?

DON: Ever thought about marrying her?

PHILIP: No. Why?

19

DON: She's very fond of you, you know.

PHILIP: Really?

DON: Yes. I was talking to her about you the other day and I could see she was very fond of you.

PHILIP: Why, what did she say?

DON: Well, I can't remember exactly, nothing specific, it was just the way she talked about you. I'm sure she'd marry you like a shot if you asked her.

PHILIP: Do you think so?

DON: I'm sure of it.

PHILIP: She hasn't said anything to me about it.

DON: Well, she has her pride.

(Silence. PHILIP *broods.)*

PHILIP: And you think I should marry her instead of Celia?

DON: I didn't say that. I wouldn't dream of saying that.

PHILIP: But you think it.

DON: I'm just saying it would be possible if you wanted to do it.

PHILIP: Well, I don't.

DON: I know you don't. I'm sorry I mentioned it.

PHILIP: That's all right.

DON: I have this theory which I think is rather attractive. I think we're only capable of loving people who are fundamentally incompatible with us.

PHILIP: That's horrible.

DON: But attractive.

PHILIP: It's not really a very helpful thing to say.

DON: Take no notice. You know very well that unless you're a scientist, it's much more important for a theory to be shapely, than for it to be true.

*(*CELIA *enters.)*

CELIA: That'll be all right for a few minutes, now. *(She helps herself to a Scotch.)* Christ, I need a drink.

(She sinks into a chair.)

DON: Did you find the lemons?

CELIA: Yes. Thanks.

20

DON: Isn't she marvellous?

(PHILIP *eyes* DON *uneasily.*)

PHILIP: I think so.

CELIA: So do I. I can't bear cooking: and I cook. I can't bear working: and I work. (*She smiles.*) And I can't bear Philip: and I'm marrying him.

PHILIP: It's all part of one basic condition.

CELIA: What?

PHILIP: You can't bear being a woman: and you are.

(CELIA *bristles.*)

CELIA: What do you mean?

PHILIP: It was a joke.

CELIA: Not a very funny joke.

PHILIP: It was about as funny as yours.

CELIA: Mine?

PHILIP: Yes, when you said you couldn't bear me and you were marrying me.

CELIA: You think that was a joke?

PHILIP: I . . .

CELIA (*laughing*): Your trouble is you have no sense of humour.

(PHILIP *is bested.*)

PHILIP: Sorry.

(*A knock at the door and* BRAHAM *enters. He is a tall, good-looking man, fashionably and expensively dressed. He carries a large paper bag.*)

BRAHAM: I hope I've come to the right place. (*He sees* CELIA.) Ah, hello, love. (*He turns to* DON.) You must be Philip.

PHILIP: No, I'm Philip.

DON: I'm Don.

BRAHAM: Oh, yes, we've met, haven't we? Well, I'm Braham. Very nice of you to invite me.

PHILIP: It's kind of you to come.

BRAHAM (*turning to* CELIA): I went down to the market to buy you some flowers, my love, but they didn't seem to have any. So I got you this instead. (*With a flourish, he produces a cauliflower from the paper bag.*) As a token of my esteem.

CELIA (*dubiously*): Thanks.

BRAHAM: I'm sure you'll be able to find a niche for it.

(CELIA *takes it from him.*)

CELIA: I'll put it in the kitchen.

BRAHAM: Just the place.

(CELIA *goes out.*)

PHILIP: Can I get you a drink?

BRAHAM: Lovely girl.

PHILIP: Sherry or Scotch?

BRAHAM (*abstractedly*): Yes, please. (*He looks over towards the kitchen, as* PHILIP *stands by the drinks table, helpless with indecision.*) Lovely. She tells me you're getting married.

PHILIP: Yes. Erm . . . ? (*His courage fails him.*)

BRAHAM: What?

PHILIP: Nothing.

(*He decides on Scotch and pours it shakily.* BRAHAM *sits down.*)

BRAHAM: Well well well.

(*Silence.* PHILIP *hands him the glass.*)

BRAHAM: I observe that you are left-handed and that your maternal granny stands, or rather stood, six foot three in her socks.

PHILIP: Er . . .

BRAHAM: How can I tell, I hear you cry. (PHILIP *exchanges a slightly desperate glance with* DON *as* BRAHAM *sips his drink.* PHILIP *smiles weakly.*) I can see it in your . . . Did I ask for Scotch?

PHILIP: Well . . .

BRAHAM: Funny, I thought I said sherry.

PHILIP: Let me . . .

BRAHAM: No, no, never mind, never mind. Think nothing of it.

(*Silence.* PHILIP *takes a cigarette box from the table and offers one to* BRAHAM.)

PHILIP: Do you smoke?

(BRAHAM *takes one.*)

BRAHAM: Thank you.

(PHILIP *hands one to* DON. *Then closes the box and lights their cigarettes as he speaks, nervously.*)

PHILIP: I gave up last summer. It was months before I could make up my mind, but I finally decided I was more nervous about dying of cancer than I would be if I gave up smoking.

BRAHAM: Well, naturally.

PHILIP: No, no, what I mean is that I decided that the degree of nervousness I suffer in everyday life under normal circumstances without smoking although it was alleviated by smoking together with the added nervousness caused by the threat of ultimate cancer came to a sum total of nervousness it seemed to me in the end and after lengthy as I say consideration greater than the original nervousness which had in the first place prompted me to take up smoking. If you follow my meaning.

(CELIA *has re-entered during this speech.*)

BRAHAM: I'm not sure I do.

PHILIP: No, well, I'm not expressing myself very well. I just mean it was paradoxical that I took up smoking because I thought it would be good for my nerves and discovered that even though it was I was more nervous after I'd taken it up than before because of the . . .

BLACKOUT
(*Aria: "Be joyful in the Lord" from Handel's "Jubilate".*)

THREE

After dinner. PHILIP, DON, CELIA, LIZ *and* ARAMINTA *are relaxing, talking, drinking coffee, brandy, etc., and smoking.* ARAMINTA, *a rather large girl with a dramatically low-cut dress sits on the floor, drinking crème de menthe.* LIZ, *a quiet, reserved girl (she does not in fact speak during the course of the scene) is dressed more soberly, and sits watching, smiling to herself from time to time.*

BRAHAM: Tell me, what is the official line on Christ's navel?

ARAMINTA: On what?

BRAHAM: Christ's navel. When I went down to London on the train the other day, I fell into conversation with this priest, a very sprightly old gent, who told me that one of his proudest achievements was a polemic he'd written some years before against the view, which he said was widely held, that Christ had had no navel.

CELIA: Why shouldn't he have had a navel?

BRAHAM: Oh, well, it's all to do with the mysterious circumstances of his birth.

CELIA: Oh, I see.

BRAHAM: Anyway, he was a marvellous old boy. Marvellous. He said he lamented the passing of the closed compartment, no-corridor train and I asked him why and he told me that years and years ago, before he'd taken up the cloth and was sowing the occasional wild oat, he'd managed to strike up an acquaintance with a boy, seduce him and suck him off, all in the course of a journey between Bognor Regis and Littlehampton.

DON: Really?

BRAHAM: Yes.

ARAMINTA: Wonderful.

PHILIP: Er, shall we have the ten o'clock news?

BRAHAM: Why?

PHILIP: Well, I was just wondering what's happened about the
Prime Minister and the government, you know . . .

BRAHAM: Oh, no, I think that would be unnecessarily depressing.

PHILIP: I just thought . . .

BRAHAM: In the car on the way over I heard them say the
Queen had sent for the Minister of Sport.

ARAMINTA: What for?

CELIA: Her trampoline needs re-stringing.

ARAMINTA: Who is the Minister of Sport, anyway?

DON: Edith somebody, isn't it?

ARAMINTA: Why's she been sent for?

BRAHAM: Well, presumably she's the senior uninjured Minister.

ARAMINTA: They're not going to make her Prime Minister, are
they?

BRAHAM: No, they can't possibly. I don't know, though, it
might be rather diverting if they did. I must say, the great
thing about all this is it shows we're accepting our
decadence with a certain stylishness.

DON: What do you mean?

BRAHAM: Well, I think most people would agree that this has
become a fairly sophisticated country. But I've always
thought of sophistication as rather a feeble substitute for
decadence. I mean I'm not saying everyone should go
round assassinating people, but you must admit the way
this man went about it did show a kind of rudimentary
dramatic flair.

DON: I'd say he was a lunatic.

BRAHAM: Oh, yes, very probably. But like a lot of lunatics he's
got one or two very shrewd ideas rattling around in his
head.

DON: Like what?

BRAHAM: Like accepting our decadence without trying to go on

25

pretending we're morally superior to the rest of the world. Like realizing that Socialism is about as much use to this country as . . . a pogo-stick to a paraplegic.

DON: That's an extraordinarily repulsive image.

BRAHAM: What? Oh, yes, I suppose it is, really. Sorry, it just sprang to mind.

ARAMINTA: I thought it was very expressive.

BRAHAM: Thank you, Araminta.

DON: Do you really think that? About socialism?

BRAHAM: My dear chap, what I think about socialism is neither here nor there. Listen, when I was younger, I was a passionate Lefty writing all kinds of turgid, earth-shaking stuff which was designed to set the world to rights and which no publisher would have touched with a pitchfork. But eventually I realized, and what a moment of five-star disillusionment that was, that it wasn't going to work. Governments would not tumble at the scratch of my quill. I was just one little person in this enormous bloody world. God, in his infinite wisdom, had given me the ability to create essentially frivolous entertainments, which were enjoyed by enough essentially frivolous people for me to be able to amble comfortably through life. Naturally, it distresses me that people are wasting their energies killing each other all over the world, and of course I'm sorry thousands of Indians starve to death every year, but I mean that's their problem, isn't it, if they will go in for all this injudicious fucking. I actually used to think that in some obscure way it was my fault.

DON: You've got over that, now, have you?

BRAHAM: Well, I have, yes. Nowadays, if I get one of those things through my letter-box telling me I can feed an entire village for a week for the price of a prawn cocktail, I tear it up, throw it in my waste-paper basket, go out to my favourite restaurant and order a prawn cocktail.

DON: And do you find that amusing?

BRAHAM: Oh, come now, the next thing you're going to say is

what if everybody was like me. Fortunately for the world and even more fortunately for me, not everybody is. Look, if I actually get a concrete chance to help people, then I do.

ARAMINTA: Yes, I saw that TV appeal you did a few weeks ago.

DON: What was that for?

BRAHAM: Twenty-five guineas.

DON: I meant, on behalf of whom.

BRAHAM: I know you did.

DON: Well?

BRAHAM (*playing up*): Oh, I don't know, it was an appeal on behalf of spavined children. Or something equally sordid.

DON: And did it raise much money?

BRAHAM: Enough to cover my fee.

DON: I'm sorry . . . I must say I find that rather disgusting.

BRAHAM: That's perfectly all right. Most people do. (*Pause. He turns sharply to* PHILIP.) Do you think I'm disgusting?

PHILIP: Er . . . no, I don't think so, no.

BRAHAM (*to* ARAMINTA): Do you?

ARAMINTA: Oh, no.

BRAHAM (*to* LIZ): You?

(LIZ *shakes her head.*)

BRAHAM (*to* CELIA): What about you?

CELIA (*smiling*): No.

BRAHAM (*turning back to* DON): There you are, you see, that's quite a good average. Obviously, my living depends on disgusting a certain percentage of people. If I didn't disgust at least a substantial minority, I wouldn't be controversial, and if I wasn't controversial, I wouldn't be rich.

DON: That's the way it works, is it?

BRAHAM: More or less.

DON: And that's the purpose of it all, to be rich?

BRAHAM: I don't know whether it's the purpose or not, but it's the result. I used to feel terribly shifty about all the money I was making, but then I realized I belonged to that small class of people who make exactly what they deserve. I'm a product. If the public stop wanting me, I stop earning.

CELIA: But you're all right for the time being.

BRAHAM: Oh, yes.

ARAMINTA: What's the best thing about being a writer?

BRAHAM: Ah, well, the real bonus comes when one actually discovers one or two moral precepts lurking about at the back of one's head. Then one can base a book on them and enjoy the illusion that one has bought one's E-type with a couple of really valuable insights, golden truths, you might say. (*He laughs heartily.*)

DON: Well, at least no one could accuse you of being self-righteous.

BRAHAM: No, but I think one would be forced to admit I was pretty complacent. What I mean is there's no point in feeling guilty about these things, there's only two alternatives, keep it or give it all away, and that's a very interesting proposition, as the rich man said to Christ, but don't call me, I'll call you.

CELIA: And egotistical too, I suppose that's necessary.

BRAHAM: Oh, absolutely. Self-obsession combined with the ability to hold opposite points of view with equal conviction. The marvellous thing is that if the internal logic is coherent, I know that even if I'm wrong, I'm right. Makes me what you might call an existentialist's nightmare.

DON: Or a hypocritical creep, some might have it.

BRAHAM: Yes. (*He shakes with laughter.*) Oh, God, I did upset some poor little journalist the other day. "How would you describe your job?" she said, and I said, "Well, I suppose you might describe it as a kind of subsidized masturbation."

DON: Don't you really think any better of it than that?

BRAHAM: Certainly not. I hope you're not implying there's anything wrong with masturbation.

DON: Well, I, no, not exactly . . .

BRAHAM: I should hope not. Masturbation is the thinking man's television. Don't you agree?

DON: I can't say I really remember.

28

BRAHAM: You shock me. (*He turns to* PHILIP.) You're not like that, are you?

PHILIP: No. I mean, well, occasionally, sometimes, I do.

BRAHAM: I'm pleased to hear it. It's extremely good for you, you know. Ah, many's the time I've had to lay down the pen and slip off to the bog for a quick one. Always remembering the Dunkirk spirit. Never forgetting that Waterloo was won in the dormitories of Eton. Any more brandy, is there?

(PHILIP *pours* BRAHAM *a brandy, then sees to the other guests.*)

CELIA (*to* DON): Wasn't that your pupil's problem?

DON: Who?

CELIA: The one who's just been sent down.

DON: Who, Boot? No, no, no, I don't think it was sexual fantasy that finished him off, it was the failure of his political fantasies.

BRAHAM: Ah, well, there you are, you see, that's what I mean.

DON: Very sad case, was Boot. James Boot. The more subtle of his colleagues used to call him Jack. His first year he was very quiet, very shy, and all his work was carefully done and scrupulously on time. Good, solid, second-class stuff. Then, the beginning of this term, he didn't turn up when we were fixing the schedules, and one of the others told me he was in bed. So I sent him a note telling him when to come for the first tutorial and what to do. But when the time arrived I got a note from him saying he couldn't come, he was in bed. I naturally assumed he was ill, so when I was next in college I thought I'd call in on him to see how he was. He's got one of those nasty new modern little rooms, and I knocked on the door and went in. It was about four o'clock in the afternoon, he was in bed, the curtains were drawn, the fire was on and the stench was incredible. We talked for a bit. He offered me a biscuit. Then, anxious to beat a hasty retreat, I said I hoped he would be better soon. Then he told me there was nothing

29

wrong with him.

It seems he'd spent the long vacation studying various
political and economic works which had plunged him into
such a state of total despair, that he had decided to devise
some kind of final solution. At the beginning of term he had
laid in enormous supplies of soup, cornflakes, biscuits,
coffee and sugar—and then gone to bed. Since then, he'd
been in bed twenty-two hours a day, brooding, only getting
up to fix himself a meal, and never leaving the room except
for the odd trip to the lavatory. "But, Boot," I said, "but,
Boot, why this sudden interest in politics? It's not even
your faculty. Can't you, don't you think it would really be
better, to turn your attention back to Wordsworth?"
Wordsworth, he said, with some passion, had nothing to
do with anything, and his work, like all art, was a lot of
self-indulgent shit which had no relevance to our problems
and was no help at all to man or beast. I must say, the
way he put it, it sounded quite convincing. I said to him:
"Look, it's not necessary to upset yourself like this. No
one's expecting you to come up with an answer to all the
problems of Western democracy." "Yes, they are," he said,
"I am." Further discussion seemed pointless. So I left him.

CELIA: And what happened?

DON: Well, he stayed in bed for the next six weeks, sending
polite notes whenever he was supposed to be turning up
somewhere, and I did nothing about it, because, because I
rather admired him. And finally he reached a decision. He
arrived at a conclusion.

He got out of bed one afternoon, took all his books
down from the shelves, and piled them up in the middle of
the room. Then he added all his papers and notes, wrapped
the whole bundle up in his gown and set fire to it. He also
set fire to the curtains, and turned the gas on. Then he put
his dressing-gown on and left the building. A couple of his
friends saw him wandering about and asked him jovially
what he was doing up at that time of day. He told them

30

he'd just set fire to the college. They carried on their way with much merry laughter. A moment later his windows blew out.

BRAHAM: Was there much damage done?

DON: His room was gutted. A little later they came to take him away. He's been formally sent down, which I think was quite unnecessary. I understand that since he's been admitted, he's been quite unable to move.

CELIA: I think that's very sad.

BRAHAM: I'd say he has a promising career ahead of him.

ARAMINTA: What as?

BRAHAM: A literary critic.

DON: I should think that's highly unlikely.

BRAHAM: I don't know. He sounds ideal. Do you know, I was actually forced to write a letter to some wretch a few weeks ago. He said my novel was too clever by half. So I wrote and said judging by the prose style of your review, I am forced to conclude, sir, that on the contrary, you are too stupid by half. Kindly leave the T.L.S. (*He laughs.*)

DON: I really don't see what that has to do with Boot.

BRAHAM: Now you come to mention it, I suppose there is no logical connection. I forgot we were subject to the austere disciplines of academic tradition. I hope you're not going to give me fifty lines. (*He makes a mock appeal to* CELIA.) Are they all like this?

CELIA: No, Don is in a class of his own. He's the only one of my tutors who hasn't made a pass at me.

BRAHAM: Really?

CELIA: Yes. I don't count Philip, of course. Anyway, he doesn't teach me.

PHILIP: You're not going to tell me Professor Burrows made a pass at you?

CELIA: Ah, no, well I've made an interesting discovery about Professor Burrows. Professor Burrows is actually dead.

PHILIP: What do you mean?

CELIA: Well, I happened to see him with his wife just before one

31

of those lectures he's been giving for decades, and she had her hand up inside his gown. Strange, I thought, and it was only later that it dawned on me what she was doing: she was winding him up. After that everything became clear—his voice, his colouring, the fact that he never takes any notice of what anyone says in seminars. He's been dead for years. They've installed a tape-recorder between his ears, and Mrs. B. stacks him away in the 'fridge every night. That's it. It explains everything, the syllabus, everything. He's a contemporary of Beowulf.

DON: Who does that leave?

PHILIP: Johnson.

DON: Oh, inevitably.

CELIA (*to* BRAHAM): Johnson is the Young Lion. He's a six-before-breakfast man. He lectures on Keats with such vigour and verve that the sticky young girls in the front row believe he is Keats. He's your typical Establishment misfit.

DON: And was he stylish about it?

CELIA: Stylish? It was one of the clumsiest gropes I've undergone for a long time. At the beginning of the tutorial, he poured me a drink and came and sat next to me on the sofa, and I thought this is it, fasten your seat belts. But he was just terribly nervous, he sat there looking strained and burbling on about the Romantics for three-quarters of an hour, and then suddenly he grabbed my further shoulder and wrenched me round so abruptly I emptied my sherry all over his camel-hair trousers. That threw him for a second. But he obviously had the sentence all worked out and he told me he thought I was very beautiful, and would I have dinner with him. I said I thought he'd better go and change his trousers before the next tutorial or his pupils would think he'd been at the Swinburne again.'

BRAHAM: How did he handle that?

CELIA: Badly. Poor man, he was desperately embarrassed. He's never stopped apologizing ever since. I quite like him now.

Rather him than Noakes any day.

DON: Noakes? (*He is amused at the thought.*)

CELIA (*to* BRAHAM): Noakes, I must tell you, is not one of the world's ten best. In fact, he looks as if he's escaped off the side of Notre Dame. His face is enormous. And he sweats profusely, which makes him a very . . . shiny man. Ice-hockey matches could be played on his forehead. He's also kind of Neanderthal, I mean his knuckles scrape along the pavement as he walks. He's a college politician, which means his tongue is long enough to reach places other people don't even know exist. I tell you, at college meetings, or cocktail parties he lurches from one important man to another, leaving a trail like a slug. Fortunately, his flattery is so grotesquely and transparently insincere, only about three-quarters of the old cretins are taken in by it. I must say, though, his grope was a great deal more thorough than Johnson's. Fortunately, his palms are so slimy, he wasn't able to get a proper purchase, as they say. But it was very nasty. He is, in every sense, oleaginous.

ARAMINTA: I think he's rather sweet.

CELIA: *Chacun à son goût.*

ARAMINTA: What do you mean?

CELIA (*feigning innocence*): Nothing.

BRAHAM: He certainly sounds extraordinarily repulsive.

ARAMINTA: I think she's exaggerating.

BRAHAM: No, no, he sounds very familiar to me. (*To* PHILIP.) What do you think about all this?

PHILIP: What?

BRAHAM: All your colleagues leching after your fionce.

PHILIP: Oh, well, I think it's quite understandable. I don't really mind.

BRAHAM: Don't you? I'm sure I would.

PHILIP: I don't know, you know . . .

BRAHAM: How come you don't teach her? Is there some fifteenth-century statute against seeing your betrothed in school hours?

PHILIP: No, the thing is, I teach philology which is sort of
optional, and old texts and things like that, which she
doesn't do because she's a graduate.

BRAHAM: Philology?

PHILIP: Yes.

BRAHAM: My God, I thought that went out years ago.

PHILIP: No.

BRAHAM: I seem to remember it as the only subject which
cunningly combined the boredom of the science faculties
with the uselessness of the arts faculties.

PHILIP: Well . . .

BRAHAM: The worst of both cultures.

PHILIP: Most people seem to think that way. But I . . . find it
interesting.

BRAHAM: Why? How?

PHILIP: Words. Words as objects. The development of words.
Abuse of words. Words illustrating civilization. I mean, I
can't go into it now, but all this new work that's being
done in structural linguistics, I find absolutely fascinating.

BRAHAM: Structural linguistics, what's that, a yet more
complicated method of over-simplification?

PHILIP: You might say so.

BRAHAM: You say you can't go into it now. Does that mean
you don't think I could grasp it?

PHILIP: I'm sure you could grasp it, I just don't think it would
interest you very much.

BRAHAM: Yes, you may be right.

PHILIP: But it does make me notice things. For instance, you're
supposed to be, I mean you are, a successful writer, you
make your living out of stringing words together. So it's
very interesting for me to try to see how your language is
formed.

BRAHAM: And how is it formed?

PHILIP: Well, I noticed just now you said something was
extraordinarily repulsive, and I thought that was very
revealing because it was a phrase Don used a few minutes

34

ago.

BRAHAM: What are you getting at?

PHILIP: Well, it shows your ability for picking out and retaining
striking phrases, subconsciously of course, but . . .

BRAHAM: Actually, as a matter of fact . . .

PHILIP (*enthusiastically*): See, that's another thing, the word
"actually", you use it a great deal.

BRAHAM: Why shouldn't I?

PHILIP: No reason why you shouldn't, you just do.

BRAHAM: I think you're being subtly insulting.

PHILIP: No, not at all, I . . .

BRAHAM: Yes, you are, go on, why don't you admit it?

PHILIP: I'm not.

BRAHAM: I think there's nothing cruder than an excess of
subtlety.

PHILIP: No, look, I'm just making an observation. Like what
you just said. That's something else. Your use of paradox.
You've got it down to a fine art, it's a reflex action. You've
digested that it's an extremely simple and extremely effective
technique.

BRAHAM: You are being insulting!

(*Silence.* BRAHAM *is angry,* PHILIP *somewhat upset. The
others are becoming embarrassed.*)

PHILIP: No.

(*Silence.*)

CELIA: He's not. He's just obsessed with the way people talk,
that's all. Sometimes I think he's more interested in that
than in what they actually say.

BRAHAM: What they what?

CELIA: Actually say.

BRAHAM (*triumphantly, to* PHILIP): See, I'm not the only one.

PHILIP: No, I know. Celia uses it quite often as well.

BRAHAM (*to Celia*): You're obviously my kind of person.

DON: Actually . . . (*He stops dead.*) Er, no, I mean, shit, yes,
why not, actually . . . God, fuckit, I've forgotten what I
was going to say now. (*Pause.*) Oh, yes, I was going to say

35

Philip is quite remarkable with words. He can give you an anagram of any word or phrase, if there is one, in about two minutes, working it out in his head.

BRAHAM: Really?

DON: Yes.

CELIA: Try him.

PHILIP: No, I don't think . . .

BRAHAM: Ah, no, you're not going to get away with it as easy as that. I want an example of this. Give me an anagram of . . . give me an anagram of "La Comédie Française". (*Silence.* PHILIP *concentrates.*)

PHILIP: In French?

BRAHAM (*magnanimously*): No, no, English will do. (*Pause. He returns his attention to the others.*) I always go there when I'm in Paris. God knows why. All that French classical theatre. Terrible camp old rubbish.

ARAMINTA: It's so stylized, isn't it?

BRAHAM (*ignoring her*): Mind you, the French never go there. Wouldn't go near it. It's full of Americans and Germans. Last time I went, I had this enormous American lady sitting next to me, and just as the lights went down, mark you, and they were banging that thing on the stage, she leant across and said, "excuse me, I haven't had time to read my programme, would you mind telling me what the play is about, because I just can't understand a word they're saying." So I said, "Well, madam, it's about a man who hates humanity so much that he would undoubtedly refuse to explain the plot of a world-famous play to an ignorant tourist."

ARAMINTA: You didn't really?

BRAHAM: She thanked me. Profusely.

ARAMINTA: Which play was it?

BRAHAM (*coldly*): Three guesses. (*He broods for a moment.*) Anyway, I hate the Frogs.

PHILIP: A defence o' racialism.

BRAHAM: What?

36

PHILIP: A defence o' racialism. It doesn't quite work. There's an f missing. But it's the best I can do.

BRAHAM (*sourly*): Wonderful.

PHILIP: Thank you.

BRAHAM: Now perhaps you'll oblige us with a fart.

DON: It's exceptionally difficult to do, that. You should try it sometime.

BRAHAM: What?

DON: That anagram game.

BRAHAM: Oh, no, if we must play games, for God's sake let them be simple.

DON: Shall we play a game?

ARAMINTA: Oo, yes, let's. What about murder?

CELIA (*maliciously*): Postman's knock.

BRAHAM: I think it's a bit late for all that. I'm for a quick hand of Emptying the Brandy Bottle, and then I must be on my way.

PHILIP (*vaguely*): I've got some carpet bowls somewhere.

BRAHAM (*handing* PHILIP *his glass*): Some other time, perhaps. (*Silence.* PHILIP *pours brandy for* BRAHAM, CELIA *and* DON, *crème de menthe for* ARAMINTA. LIZ *covers her glass with her hand.*)

ARAMINTA: Are you writing a new novel?

BRAHAM: Yes, I am. It's nearly finished.

ARAMINTA: What's it about?

BRAHAM: It's about a social worker, who, after years of unremitting toil, finally sees the light, and renounces everything to become a merchant banker. I'm going to give it a really unfashionable happy ending. It's going to finish with his marriage to a sensitive film star.

ARAMINTA: Sounds intriguing.

BRAHAM: If it does as well as the last one, I'm going to have to leave the country.

ARAMINTA: Why?

BRAHAM: Tax. The tax system is absolutely iniquitous. What do they do with it all, I don't know. You'd think they'd make some sort of reasonable allowance. After all, I am a dollar-earner.

ARAMINTA: But the system's always been weighted against artists, hasn't it?

BRAHAM: Yes, all that's in the book. Although it's mainly, as I say, about this self-sacrificing character who gives up the comforts of moral superiority for the harsh realities of high finance. Should bring foam to the lips of the progressives. It'll be one up the noses of all the self-appointed salt of the earth who preach the revolution in the happy and comfortable knowledge that it'll never come.

DON: There are some people who believe in it, you know.

BRAHAM (*acidly*): There are some people who believe in God. (*Silence.*)

DON: I don't really see what that has to do with it.

BRAHAM: No, well, never mind, perhaps you're right. (*He empties his glass.*) In any case, I must be getting along. It's been a delightful evening. (*He looks over to* CELIA.) Can I give anyone a lift? Only one of you, I'm afraid, because it's only a two-seater.

ARAMINTA: Yes, please.

BRAHAM: Er, right, O.K., where do you live?

ARAMINTA: Just round the corner, actually.

BRAHAM: Oh, well, that's all right, if it's very near by, you can squeeze in the back, and I can take someone else. (*To* CELIA.) Where do you live?

CELIA: Bradley Road.

BRAHAM: Is that far?

CELIA: About half-an-hour's walk.

BRAHAM: O.K., fine.

CELIA: I think perhaps I should stay and clear up a bit.

PHILIP: No, that's all right, love, I'll do it.

CELIA (*meaningfully*): But I'd like to stay.

PHILIP: No, it'll be quite all right, you've done enough work for this evening.

DON: Come to think of it, Araminta, it'd probably be easier if you come with me. I shall be driving Liz back.

PHILIP: I'm sorry I haven't got my car. I lent it to a friend this evening.

BRAHAM: Right, good, that's all settled then. (*He gets up, turns to* CELIA.) Shall we be off?

CELIA (*to* PHILIP): Are you sure you don't want me to stay?

PHILIP: Quite sure.

CELIA: Right then.

(BRAHAM *and* CELIA *move over to the door.*)

BRAHAM: Thanks again. Lovely to meet you. And may all your troubles be lexicological ones.

PHILIP: I'll show you out.

BRAHAM: Good night.

ARAMINTA: Good night.

DON (*charming*): Good-bye.

(PHILIP *shows them out amid general salutations.*)

DON: Miserable bugger. (*Pause. He gets up.*) Are we all ready, then?

(LIZ *gets up,* ARAMINTA *remains seated.*)

ARAMINTA: Perhaps . . . it's a terrible mess. Perhaps I'll stay and give him a hand.

DON: It's a kind thought. I don't suppose he'd let you.

ARAMINTA: I don't know, I might be able to persuade him.

(PHILIP *re-enters.*)

PHILIP: You going as well?

DON: Yes, I think we'd better.

ARAMINTA: I'm going to stay and help you clear up.

PHILIP: Oh, no, that's all right.

ARAMINTA: Then you can walk me home. How's that for a bargain?

PHILIP: Well . . .

ARAMINTA: Fresh air will do you good.

PHILIP: Well, all right, that's very kind.

(DON *and* LIZ *are by the door.* PHILIP *goes over and shows them out. Sounds of leave-taking from the hall.* ARAMINTA *starts piling plates in a fairly desultory way.* PHILIP *returns.*)

39

PHILIP: It's very good of you, this.

ARAMINTA: Nonsense. You just sit down.

(PHILIP *sinks down on to the sofa, sighing.*)

PHILIP: Just stick them in the kitchen. My man will do them tomorrow.

ARAMINTA: Tired?

PHILIP: Exhausted.

ARAMINTA: It was a great success.

(PHILIP *smiles wanly. Silence.* ARAMINTA *pauses in her work.*)

ARAMINTA: What time does he come in?

PHILIP: Who?

ARAMINTA: Your man.

PHILIP (*uneasily*): About eleven, usually.

(*Silence.* ARAMINTA *leaves the table and moves round behind the sofa to look out of the window.* PHILIP *seems anxious. After some hesitation, he steals a glance at her.*)

PHILIP: Not raining, is it?

ARAMINTA: No.

PHILIP: Oh, good.

(ARAMINTA *wanders across until she is directly behind* PHILIP. *Then, she leans forward and begins to massage his temples gently. This has the effect of making him seem even less relaxed. After a time, she moves round and sits on his knee.*)

ARAMINTA: Hello.

PHILIP: Erm, hello.

(*She kisses him.*)

ARAMINTA: Is that nice?

PHILIP: Very. Could you, could you just move down a bit?

(*She does so, and* PHILIP's *look of intense pain changes to one of acute anxiety.*)

ARAMINTA: Better?

PHILIP: Yes.

(*She kisses him again.*)

ARAMINTA: Shall we go to bed?

(*Brief silence.*)

PHILIP: I'll . . . just go and get my coat.

(ARAMINTA *stares at him for a moment in blank incompre-*
hension, then realizes what he means. She stands up.)
ARAMINTA: I meant together.
PHILIP: Oh, I wasn't quite sure.
(*Panic overcomes him. He looks at his watch, stares fixedly*
at it for a moment.)
ARAMINTA: Well?
PHILIP: Well . . .
ARAMINTA: Don't be too enthusiastic.
PHILIP: It's just . . . it's just . . .
ARAMINTA: What?
PHILIP (*clutching at a straw*): I haven't any, haven't got any . . .
ARAMINTA: Not necessary.
PHILIP: Oh.
ARAMINTA: If you don't want to, just say so——
PHILIP: No, no, I do, I do.
ARAMINTA: —and I'll go home——
PHILIP: No.
ARAMINTA: —it's not a matter of life or death to me, you know.
(PHILIP *stands up.*)
PHILIP: I know, I'm sorry, it just took me a bit by surprise,
that's all.
(*He kisses her.*)
ARAMINTA: Didn't look like a very pleasant surprise.
PHILIP: Please. (*He kisses her again.*) It's just that I'm shy, that's
all.
ARAMINTA: I know. I love shy men.
PHILIP: All right now?
ARAMINTA: Yes.
(*They embrace.*)
ARAMINTA: Is that the bedroom, through there?
PHILIP: Yes.
(*She moves across to it, turns at the door.*)
ARAMINTA: Don't be long.
(PHILIP *smiles weakly at her, as she exits, then sinks down*
on to the sofa again. A moment later he gets up, moves over

41

*to the table, takes a cigarette from the cigarette box, and
puts it in his mouth, where it hangs limply for a moment.
Then he returns it to the box, and sighs deeply.*)

PHILIP: God help us all.

(*He exits wearily and reluctantly into the bedroom, leaving
the stage empty.*)

CURTAIN

(*Aria: "O wie ängstlich" from Mozart's "Die Entführung aus
dem Serail", followed, during the interval, by the aria: "Dies
Bildnis ist bezaubernd schön" from "die Zauberflöte", and
the aria: "Wenn der Freude Tränen fliessen" from "die
Entführung."*)

FOUR

The next morning. ARAMINTA *is sitting at the table with a cup of coffee and a cigarette, reading the newspaper. There is a knock at the door. She looks up, startled.* CELIA *walks in, sees* ARAMINTA *and stops dead.* ARAMINTA *gets up, quickly. It takes her a moment to regain her composure.*

ARAMINTA: Er, hello.

CELIA: Good morning. Is Philip in, by any chance?

ARAMINTA: I believe he's in the bath.

CELIA: Oh, really? (*The shock is beginning to leave her.*) Alone?

ARAMINTA: I think so.

CELIA: You're slipping. (*She helps herself to a cigarette, lights it.*) Well, I must say, I am surprised.

ARAMINTA: Why?

CELIA: I never thought you'd manage to add Philip to your collection.

ARAMINTA: What do you mean?

CELIA: You know, I sometimes think, although I can never quite bring myself to accept it, that you really are as thick as you pretend to be.

ARAMINTA: You're very offensive, this morning.

CELIA: I'm very offended. I don't know why you couldn't have left him alone. Do you write all their names up in a Book of Remembrance, or something? Do you give every hundredth one a pair of gold cuff-links with some discreetly erotic motif? Are you thinking of turning professional?

(*Silence.*)

ARAMINTA: Would you care for some coffee?

CELIA: No, I would not.

ARAMINTA: Don't be like that.

CELIA: Why not?

ARAMINTA: It wasn't serious.

CELIA: Why did you bother, then?

ARAMINTA: That's an absurd question. I just felt like it.

CELIA: Didn't you stop to consider the consequences?

ARAMINTA: There are no consequences. At least, there wouldn't
    have been, if you hadn't walked in just now. The idea was,
    you see, that you weren't going to find out about it.

CELIA: Well, all I can say is, there's no accounting for taste.

ARAMINTA: What, his taste or my taste.

CELIA (*flustered*): His taste.

ARAMINTA: You should know, you're engaged to him.

CELIA: That's my business.

ARAMINTA: I know. I hope he gives you better service than he
    gave me.

CELIA: What do you mean?

ARAMINTA: Never mind.

CELIA: How can you be so cheap and disgusting?

ARAMINTA: Practice makes perfect.

CELIA: Yes, apparently.

ARAMINTA: And where did you spend last night?
    (*Silence.*)

CELIA: Look, will you, will you please tell Philip that I called—

ARAMINTA: Why don't you wait and tell him yourself?

CELIA: —and that I won't be calling again.

ARAMINTA: That's ridiculous, you can't mean that, I can't tell
    him that.

CELIA (*moving to the door*): Don't, then.

ARAMINTA: There's no need to be like that about it, honestly. I
    promise you, I won't be coming back for more. If that's
    the word.

CELIA: Well, neither will I.

    (CELIA *storms out.* ARAMINTA *sits down, reflects for a moment,*

44

then returns to the paper. A moment later, PHILIP *enters. He and* ARAMINTA *greet each other warily. He pours a cup of coffee, sugars and stirs it, then moves over to the window.*)

PHILIP: It's a good view, isn't it?

ARAMINTA: Yes, very nice.

PHILIP: You can see the river. In the distance. When the tide's in. (*Longish pause.*) It's out at the moment. (*Pause.*) Look, I'm sorry about last night.

ARAMINTA: No need to be.

PHILIP: Yes, it was awful, I mean, it must have been awful for you.

ARAMINTA: No, it wasn't.

PHILIP: The thing is, I suppose I was a bit taken by surprise. It's the first time that's ever happened to me.

ARAMINTA: You're not . . . you're not trying to tell me you were a virgin.

PHILIP: No, no. No, not that.

ARAMINTA: Oh, you mean, it's the first time you've not been able to make it.

PHILIP: Not that, either.

ARAMINTA: What then?

PHILIP: It's just the first time I've ever been asked like that, point-blank. I think I must have found it rather disconcerting.

ARAMINTA: And that's why you were rather . . . disconcerted.

PHILIP: Yes.

ARAMINTA: It doesn't matter at all. It happens more often than you might think. Especially the first time.

PHILIP: Oh, does it?

ARAMINTA (*breezily*): First-night nerves.

PHILIP: What a . . . colourful description.

ARAMINTA: Nothing to worry about. If at first you don't succeed . . .

(PHILIP *smiles, appalled.*)

PHILIP: Have you had some breakfast?

ARAMINTA: Coffee, I've had.

45

PHILIP: Would you like something to eat?

ARAMINTA: I don't think so, thanks.

PHILIP: I usually have an enormous breakfast.
   (*Silence.*)

ARAMINTA: Don't worry.

PHILIP: What about?

ARAMINTA: Anything. I don't mind. At least you're kind and
   gentle. It's more than can be said for most of them.

PHILIP: What do you do it for?

ARAMINTA: Company. I like being with people. And if you're
   with them, you might as well do it as not. Don't you
   agree?

PHILIP: I don't . . . disagree.

ARAMINTA: They tell me I'm a classic case, because my uncle
   raped me when I was twelve. I've never quite been able to
   see the connection, you'd think it would have put me off,
   wouldn't you?

PHILIP: Yes.

ARAMINTA: I suppose it did rather take the romance out of
   things.

PHILIP: Haven't you ever . . . been in love with anyone?

ARAMINTA: Not really. I did have an affair with a gypsy when I
   was about fifteen. I used to climb out of the window every
   night and cycle about three miles to meet him. He never
   used to say very much. I was terrified of him. It went on
   for about a month, then he moved on, and I remember
   being very sad. But I don't know that I was in love with
   him. I quite often hero-worship people, that quite often
   happens, but it's difficult to go on with once you know
   them a little . . . better.

PHILIP: And are they often cruel to you?

ARAMINTA: Oh, yes, I'd say so, what I am seems to upset them
   in some kind of way. I always seem to bring out the worst
   in people. There was one who stole my clothes when I was
   asleep one night and locked me in the bedroom of his flat
   for about three weeks. He was the worst. He hardly gave

46

me any food. He used to threaten me with a knife. Once
he nearly strangled me.

PHILIP: What happened?

ARAMINTA: Well, in the end he came and let me out. I was
nearly going mad. There seemed no logical reason why I
shouldn't be there, in that disgusting room, for ever. But
finally he let me go. It was strange. He was so abject. He
kept apologizing all the time, asking me to forgive him.
Then, when I was leaving, he asked me to marry him.

PHILIP: God.

ARAMINTA: I felt so sorry for him.

PHILIP: Yes. (*Pause.*) It must have been terrible.

ARAMINTA: I could tell you things you would never forget.
(*Silence.*)

PHILIP: Why . . . why do you do it all?

ARAMINTA: That's rather a silly question.

PHILIP: Yes, yes, it is, sorry.

ARAMINTA: I get lonely. I hate sleeping alone. All that.

PHILIP: Yes.
(*He smiles at her. She gets up.*)

ARAMINTA: Well, I suppose I'd better get dressed.

PHILIP: Yes, I'll fix some breakfast. What would you like?
(ARAMINTA *takes his hand.*)

ARAMINTA: Come on.

PHILIP: What?

ARAMINTA: We'll be all right this time.
(PHILIP *hesitates. A moment of private dilemma.*)

PHILIP No.

ARAMINTA: No?

PHILIP: Really.
(ARAMINTA *lets go his hand.*)

ARAMINTA: Well, all right.

PHILIP: No, listen, I think I'd better explain.

ARAMINTA: There's no point in explaining, love, you either want
to or you don't.

PHILIP: No, I mean about last night.

47

ARAMINTA: I've told you . . .

PHILIP: I know it was my fault, I was very weak-minded.

ARAMINTA: Weak-minded, was it?

PHILIP: I should never have agreed, I knew it would be a disaster.

ARAMINTA: Well, I could see you were thrown by the directness of my approach.

PHILIP: It wasn't that, it was just, I didn't really want to.

ARAMINTA: I know, it's funny how important fidelity is to some people. I mean, it's something that never occurs to me.

PHILIP: It wasn't that, the truth is, I don't really find you attractive.

(*Silence.*)

ARAMINTA: I see.

PHILIP: No, don't be upset, it's my fault, my taste has always been terribly limited.

ARAMINTA (*upset*): I'm not upset.

PHILIP: No . . .

ARAMINTA: I don't know why you should think that.

PHILIP: It's just . . .

ARAMINTA: I mean, I don't exactly find you irresistible.

PHILIP: No. I'm sorry about it all.

ARAMINTA: So you should be.

PHILIP: Yes.

ARAMINTA: It might have been easier if you'd said last night.

PHILIP: Yes.

ARAMINTA: Don't you think?

PHILIP: Yes.

ARAMINTA: I don't know, who do you think you are?

PHILIP: Well . . .

ARAMINTA: Anyway, I shan't offend your sight much longer.

PHILIP: You don't offend my sight . . .

ARAMINTA: I'll get dressed and leave you alone.

PHILIP: . . . that's not it at all.

ARAMINTA: Won't take me a minute.

PHILIP: Please.

ARAMINTA: A lot of people do find me attractive.

PHILIP: I'm sure. It's just me. I can't seem to like women unless they're . . .

ARAMINTA: There's no need to go into it.

PHILIP: No, all right.

ARAMINTA: Not that you did.

(*She moves off towards the bedroom.*)

PHILIP: Can I get you some breakfast?

ARAMINTA: Will you please stop parroting on about breakfast?

(ARAMINTA *exits.* PHILIP *stands disconsolately for a minute, then pours himself a huge bowl of cornflakes, adding sugar and milk. He is about to begin eating when* ARAMINTA *returns, having dressed with extraordinary speed.*)

ARAMINTA: There is just one other thing.

PHILIP: Look, please don't go.

ARAMINTA: There is one other thing I should mention to you.

PHILIP: What?

ARAMINTA: When you were in the bath.

PHILIP: Yes.

ARAMINTA: Celia.

PHILIP: What?

ARAMINTA: Called.

PHILIP: God. Why didn't you tell me?

ARAMINTA: I just have.

PHILIP: What . . . what did she say?

ARAMINTA: She seemed a bit put out.

PHILIP: Put out?

ARAMINTA: Yes. She asked me to tell you she wouldn't be calling again.

PHILIP: What?

ARAMINTA: That was it, I think.

PHILIP: Why?

ARAMINTA: Well, as far as I could gather, it's not to do with your religious beliefs.

PHILIP: What?

ARAMINTA: Why do you think, you half-witted buffoon?

PHILIP: Because you were here. (ARAMINTA *does not answer.*)
Oh, God.
ARAMINTA: Passion.
PHILIP: I don't know what to do.
ARAMINTA: No, I'm sure you don't.
(*She moves over to the door.*)
PHILIP: Wait. What did she say?
ARAMINTA: Well, naturally we discussed the weather. Then, as I
remember, she became rather impolite. (PHILIP *groans.*
ARAMINTA *softens.*) Look, I'm sorry it happened. There
was nothing I could do about it. I think I'd better
go now.
(*She does so.* PHILIP *stands for a moment, uncertain. Then
he picks up the 'phone, dials a five-figure number and waits.
No answer. He puts the 'phone down. He wanders back to
to the table, sits down, picks up the bowl of cornflakes and
starts eating.*)

BLACKOUT

(*Chorus: "Vollendet ist das grosse Werk" from Haydn's "die
Schöpfung".*)

FIVE

PHILIP *is sitting at his desk, working, later that day. A knock at the door.* CELIA *walks in.* PHILIP *gets up quickly. They look at each other for a moment, distraught.*

PHILIP: Love.
CELIA: I just came back to tell you I wasn't coming back.
PHILIP: I've been trying to 'phone you all day.
CELIA: I've been out.
PHILIP: Working?
CELIA: No, of course not, what do you think I am?
PHILIP: I . . .
CELIA: I suppose you've been working.
PHILIP: Yes.
CELIA: Typical.
PHILIP: I thought it would take my mind off things.
CELIA: And did it?
PHILIP: No.
CELIA: Even more typical.
PHILIP: Why?
CELIA: Did you hear what I said?
PHILIP: What?
CELIA: When I came in.
PHILIP: Yes, but listen . . .
CELIA: If you say "I can explain everything," I'll punch your bloody teeth in.
PHILIP: But I can.
CELIA: I suppose you were discussing morphology all night. Or checking her vowel sounds.

51

PHILIP: No.

CELIA: It's so insulting, Philip. I mean you deliberately got rid of me.

PHILIP: What do you mean?

CELIA: Well, I did ask you to let me stay.

PHILIP: You didn't.

CELIA: Of course I did. I couldn't have made it much clearer if I'd started unbuttoning myself.

PHILIP: But I thought you just wanted to help with the washing-up.

CELIA: You amaze me. You really do.

PHILIP: Christ, I wish you had stayed.

CELIA: Why?

PHILIP: I didn't realize you wanted to stay the night. Oh, God, I wish you had.

(*Silence.*)

CELIA: You're being cunning.

PHILIP: I'm not.

CELIA: Don't. It's most unlike you.

PHILIP: I'm not.

CELIA: Look.

PHILIP: What?

CELIA: If you didn't let me stay because you thought I wanted to do the washing-up, why did you let her stay when you thought she wanted to do the washing-up?

PHILIP: She insisted.

CELIA: And more to the point, why did you let her stay when you realized she didn't want to do the washing-up?

PHILIP: She insisted.

CELIA: And you gave in.

PHILIP: Yes.

CELIA: Well, why?

PHILIP: Because I didn't want to hurt her feelings.

CELIA: What about my feelings?

PHILIP: You weren't there.

CELIA: If you go on saying things like that to me, do you really

52

expect I'm going to marry you?

PHILIP: I hope so.

CELIA: You're so incredibly . . . bland. You just sit there like a pudding, wobbling gently.

PHILIP: Do I?

CELIA: You're about as emotional as a pin-cushion.

PHILIP: I don't think that's true.

CELIA: Don't you?

PHILIP: No, I don't think so.

CELIA: Only you would sit there pondering the pros and cons of a fairly conventional simile.

PHILIP: It's more of a hyperbole really, isn't it?

CELIA: It's more of a fucking insult, that's what it really is, I think you'll find. Seeking a response, not a bloody inquest.

PHILIP: Oh, well . . .

CELIA: Inviting a retort, not a sodding debate.

PHILIP: I . . .

CELIA: You're talking about last night as if it were a conference on the future of the phoneme.

PHILIP: Am I?

CELIA: You're not even sorry!

PHILIP: Of course I am. Of course I am.

(*By now,* CELIA *is angry and upset.*)

CELIA: I'm going.

PHILIP: No, don't.

CELIA: I've said what I came to say.

PHILIP: Don't go before I tell you what happened.

CELIA: I know what happened, I don't want to hear the squalid details. I don't want to listen to your pathetic attempts at self-justification.

PHILIP: I'm not trying to justify myself. I just want to explain to you exactly what happened. Then you can make your mind up.

CELIA: All right, go on, tell me. (*Pause.*) Try to make it as entertaining as possible.

53

PHILIP: Well . . . well . . . she asked me to go to bed with her, just like that. It took me so much by surprise, I could think of no delicate way to refuse. So I accepted. The whole thing was a complete fiasco. No good at all. Then, this morning she suggested we try again, and I had to tell her it was no use, because I quite honestly didn't find her attractive.

CELIA: Not many laughs in that.

PHILIP: No. No, I suppose there weren't.

CELIA: What happened next?

PHILIP: She left.

CELIA: Immediately?

PHILIP: Yes. She seemed very angry.

CELIA: Fancy that.

PHILIP: I handled it badly.

CELIA: You might say so. Sounds to me like a triumph of emotional incompetence.

PHILIP: Well, that's how it happened.

CELIA: And I suppose you think that makes it all right, do you?

PHILIP: What do you mean?

CELIA: I suppose you think because you were bullied into doing something you then failed to do anyway, it's as if the whole thing didn't happen.

PHILIP: No.

CELIA: Did it never occur to you that I might prefer it if you brazened the whole thing out and said, yes, it was all planned, it was your final fling before we got married, or something like that?

PHILIP: But it wasn't.

CELIA: You're so damn literal-minded. I mean you might have just said you'd done it and you were sorry and it wouldn't happen again—instead of saying all right, not to worry, I was an abject failure, so that doesn't count.

PHILIP: I didn't say that.

CELIA: No, you didn't even say that.

54

PHILIP: All I can do is tell you what happened and leave it up to you.

CELIA: Well, if you leave it up to me, I shall have to say I can't possibly undertake to spend my life with someone so hopelessly weak and indecisive, he's going to leave every major issue up to me.

PHILIP: That's not very fair.

CELIA: We're not playing croquet, you know.

PHILIP: No, but in this case I've made my half of the decision. I want to marry you. So it's only up to you in the sense that you haven't decided yet.

CELIA: Oh, you do make me so angry.

PHILIP: Why?

CELIA: You never understand what I'm trying to say.

PHILIP: Maybe not, but I think I usually understand what you do say.

CELIA: God, you're completely impossible.

PHILIP (*bewildered*): I'm sorry. (*Pause.*) I suppose I am indecisive. (*Pause.*) My trouble is, I'm a man of no convictions. (*Longish pause.*) At least, I think I am. (CELIA *starts laughing.*) What's the joke?

CELIA: I am fond of you.

PHILIP (*lost*): Are you?

(*Silence.*)

CELIA: I'm afraid my plan didn't work at all.

PHILIP: Plan?

CELIA: I was going to use it as an excuse. I mean it seemed like a perfectly good excuse.

PHILIP: Use what as an excuse? What for?

CELIA: For . . . finishing.

PHILIP: I don't understand.

CELIA: Well, I've been thinking, you see, really, for a long time, that we aren't really compatible.

PHILIP: Oh.

CELIA: I always used to think you were just the sort of person I'd been looking for. Someone fairly intelligent and reliable

55

and kind and safe and a little bit dull. Somebody who admired me and thought what I said was worth listening to, not just worth tolerating.

PHILIP: But you were wrong.

CELIA: Yes, I think perhaps I was wrong.

PHILIP: I see.

CELIA: And after what happened last night, I thought I'd better come over to discuss things with you. And when I found Araminta here, I thought that gives me an excuse not to discuss things with you. I can just leave you, and make you think it's your fault.

PHILIP (*confused*): How do you mean, what happened last night? You didn't know about it, did you?

CELIA: I mean what happened to me.

PHILIP: Oh. What did happen to you?

CELIA: Braham took me back to his hotel.

PHILIP: Oh.

CELIA: And I stayed the night there.

PHILIP: But . . . why?

CELIA: I don't know, he went on at me. And I finally thought oh well, why not, I was still very angry about your not letting me stay. I don't know why. I felt dreadful this morning. He kept saying that creative artists had a much more consuming sexual urge than ordinary people. He told me that's why Bach had thirty children.

PHILIP: And were you convinced by this argument?

CELIA: No.

PHILIP: But you still . . . ?

CELIA: Yes.

PHILIP: Why? I don't see why.

CELIA: Well, he's so confident and self-assured, I don't know why. I just suddenly felt like it, don't go on about it.

PHILIP: And is that what you want?

CELIA: I don't know, I suppose so. Not him, I don't mean him, he's awful, but something like that.

PHILIP: What makes you think he's awful?

56

CELIA: Well, it was this morning, the way he behaved this morning, that really turned me off him. For one thing, he was so nasty about you.

PHILIP: Was he?

CELIA: Yes, he really hates you. All the time yesterday evening, he thought you were taking the piss in a particularly subtle way.

PHILIP: Really?

CELIA: And then when I'd argued with him a bit and told him that wasn't in your nature, he finally agreed and said, yes, come to think of it, he supposed you were far too boring to do anything as enterprising as that.

PHILIP: Well, he's right there, isn't he?

CELIA: What do you mean?

PHILIP: Isn't that what you think?

CELIA: Of course not, don't be so rude.

PHILIP: I'm sorry, I thought that's what you just said.

CELIA: I think you get a perverse kick out of running yourself down.

PHILIP: No, I don't. I don't think I do.

CELIA: Anyway, I defended you, even though I knew you wouldn't have defended yourself.

PHILIP: Why did he hate me, I don't know, I didn't hate him.

CELIA: Didn't you?

PHILIP: No, I thought he was quite amusing.

CELIA: And do you hate him now?

PHILIP: No.

CELIA: Not even after everything I've told you?

PHILIP: I don't suppose he's very happy.

CELIA (*angrily*): And are you happy?

PHILIP: No.

CELIA: Well then.

PHILIP: Not at the moment.

CELIA (*offended*): Oh, I see.

PHILIP: I mean . . . I mean, I hope to be. I have been. I hope I will be. (*He moves over to the window.*) Look. The tide's in.

It's a lovely day, look. (*Pause.*) It's very rare to have a day as fine as this in November.

CELIA: Yes.

PHILIP (*smiling*): Just when one was getting used to the idea of winter. (*Pause.*) I'm glad you defended me. I don't see what he has against me.

CELIA: That was only the beginning. He got far worse.

PHILIP: In what way?

CELIA: It was when he read about E. H. Formby in the paper.

PHILIP: What about him?

CELIA: Haven't you looked at the paper today?

PHILIP: No, I couldn't, it was all full of stuff about the Prime Minister, I thought it would be too upsetting.

CELIA: Well, E. H. Formby was murdered yesterday as well.

PHILIP: He wasn't!

CELIA: Yes.

PHILIP: But why?

CELIA: Well, apparently there's some gang of lunatics about, whose intention is to knock off all the most eminent English writers. You remember Harold Heath fell in front of a tube a few weeks ago?

PHILIP: Yes.

CELIA: It seems he was their first victim and E. H. Formby is their second. Look, there's this thing in the paper about it. This letter they've found. Have you got today's paper? (PHILIP *hands it to her. She rustles about for a moment.*) Here we are. They found him floating down the river, poor old soul, and then his wife handed in this letter he received a few weeks ago. Well, then they remembered Harold Heath and found *he'd* received one of them as well. They've printed the letter in full, I'll read it to you, it was one of those ones made up of newspaper clippings.
Dear Sir or Madam,

Please excuse the disagreeable format of this letter, the reasons for which will, I hope, soon become clear to you. I write on behalf of the Fellowship of Allied Terrorists

Against Literature—F.A.T.A.L.—(formerly the Fellowship of Useful and Charitable Killers), of which I am the President, to inform you that you (along with twenty-four others) have been selected as one of the victims of a series of ritual murders which I and my colleagues will be carrying out at staggered intervals over the next few months.

A word of explanation is perhaps in order. It is the opinion of myself and my associates that a great number of the disappointments and mishaps of this troubled world are the direct result of literature and the allied arts. It is our belief that no human being who devotes his life and energy to the manufacture of fantasies can be anything but fundamentally inadequate. Consequently we have decided to execute twenty-five of the most highly-regarded of your number in the firm (but faint) hope of catching the imagination of the world and encouraging the authorities, backed by the public, to continue our work on a more official and judicial basis, following the recent excellent example of other more enlightened countries. Our initial reservations about the rather vulgarly sensational aspects of our programme have been dispelled by the reflection that they pale beside the cheap and meritricious effects you regularly use to achieve your dubious aims.

The abominable Flaubert, in his otherwise spectacularly dreary and puerile novel *Madame Bovary*, did manage to struggle through, by accident or design, to one valuable insight: he shows that the ugly and pathetic tribulations of his foolish heroine are caused directly by her subjection to the crudely alluring imagery of fiction. Let me make it clear to you that we are not moralizers or censors; nor are we in any way associated with those ludicrous organizations who waste their time peevishly complaining about the tendency of modern literature to deprave and corrupt. So it does: but not in the narrow sense they mean, not by the tedious detailing of some crass sexual act beyond the emotional means and gymnastic abilities of those indignant ladies. It depraves by purveying, however concealed, some form of deceitful idealism. And it corrupts by the exaltation of a perverse individualism. In short, we are doing this because we do not think you have the right to compensate for your own inadequacies by attempting to affect the behaviour and deepen the self-doubts of other more innocent souls. Nor do we believe in the lying proposals of your neurotic mysticism; we do not seek absolute beauty in a phrase of music, or perfection in the whisper of a lover. All this is lies.

This letter, on the other hand, is the truth, as will shortly become apparent. You would be unwise to dismiss it as the work of a crank. Please do not take it too personally. I do regret the distress which will inevitably be caused, but we have come to regard this as our melancholy and unavoidable duty.

Good morning and good-bye.

> Your humble and obedient servant,
> Scardanelli.

Fascinating, isn't it?

PHILIP: Horrible.

CELIA: Anyway, Braham was transfixed by it.

PHILIP: Was he?

CELIA: He wasn't one of the twenty-five. He didn't know whether to be relieved or insulted.

PHILIP: Oh, I see.

CELIA: First of all, he was furious. He said it was quite obvious the man had no taste at all, as was apparent by the morons he'd already chosen. But that didn't really satisfy him, and finally he decided the letter hadn't reached him yet, it had gone via his agent or his publisher who were both hopeless at forwarding things and was now lying on one of his many doormats. When he saw in the paper that the police hadn't yet traced all the recipients of the letter, that more or less confirmed it for him.

PHILIP: So what happened then?

CELIA: I had to walk home, that's what happened.

PHILIP: Why?

CELIA: Because he decided they were after him. He was convinced there was a sniper with a telescopic sight in the building across the road, waiting for him to step out of the hotel. Humphrey Bogart, he was, the Man Who Knew Too Much. He told me to come back and see him this evening, and I left him there, revelling in his own cowardice.

PHILIP: What's he going to do?

CELIA: I don't know, wait till he grows a beard and go out the back door, I expect. "I shall have to leave the country," he kept saying.

PHILIP: Are you going to see him this evening?

CELIA: Certainly not. I did consider turning up in a black mask with a water pistol, but I decided against it. Walking back, it occurred to me he'd made it all up to economize on the petrol. He's an exceptionally mean man.

PHILIP: What makes you think that?

CELIA: Oh, I can tell, he's obsessed with money, he's always talking about money. He's got that "that'll be fourpence" look when he offers you a cigarette.

PHILIP: So you're not going.

CELIA: No, I told you.

PHILIP: Come back, then. (*He smiles.*) All is forgiven.

CELIA (*bristling*): What do you mean?

PHILIP: I don't know. Joke, really.

CELIA: Oh.

PHILIP: But, I mean, I mean it.

CELIA: I've thought about it a lot.

PHILIP: I know. . . .

CELIA: I've made up my mind.

PHILIP: Why?

CELIA: I think we'd probably make each other very unhappy.

PHILIP: Why?

CELIA: Because I don't think you'd be able to control me.

61

PHILIP: Does that matter?

CELIA: I didn't think so at first. In fact, to begin with, I thought that was the great advantage. But I don't any more.

PHILIP: Perhaps you're right.

CELIA: You see, that's the thing, you're so unassertive. Perhaps you're right! Is that the best you can do?

PHILIP: All right, I'm not going to let you leave me.

CELIA: It's no good doing it now, is it, it's supposed to be spontaneous.

PHILIP: Well, I only said perhaps you're right because I was trying to look at it from your point of view. I mean, it's quite obvious what I see in you, isn't it? It's much more of a mystery what you see in me, and if you don't see what you did see any more, then perhaps you *are* right. If you see what I mean.

CELIA: No.

PHILIP: I'm not surprised you are having second thoughts, if all these people keep making passes at you all the time.

CELIA: What are you talking about?

PHILIP: Well, you know, Noakes and Johnson and all those people you were talking about last night.

CELIA: Oh, that.

PHILIP: Yes.

CELIA: None of that was true.

PHILIP: What?

CELIA: You know I'm always making things up.

PHILIP: Why?

CELIA: Well, you've got to say something, haven't you? Can't just sit there like a statue all evening. Like Liz. And lies are usually that much more interesting than the truth, that's all.

PHILIP: Oh. (*Pause.* PHILIP *considers this.*) Well, if that's the case, can't we try to come to some arrangement? I mean, I could try—or pretend—to be firmer, and you could pretend not to mind my weakness so much.

CELIA: No. Of course not.

PHILIP: Why not?

CELIA: What a monstrous suggestion.

PHILIP: Why?

CELIA: Well, it's . . . it's so deceitful. (PHILIP *laughs*.) No, look, it's different telling a few stories to liven up the party, from basing your whole life on a lie.

PHILIP: You just said lies were more interesting than the truth.

CELIA: You're being literal-minded again.

(*Silence*.)

PHILIP: I don't know. I've always been a failure with women.

CELIA: Oh, please.

PHILIP: But it's true. I remember, I remember the first girl I was ever in love with, Carol her name was, and I made the mistake, just as we were about to go to bed together for the first time, of telling her I was a virgin. Oh, well, then, she said, that was that, she wasn't going to be a guinea-pig for anyone. It was that phrase that did it. She became so entranced and horrified by the idea represented by her own quite fortuitous image, that I gave up, there was obviously no hope. Guinea-pig, "I'm not going to be a guinea-pig," she kept on saying. So there it was. A whole relationship doomed by a random word-association. This is the same thing. You think I'm being sentimental and self-pitying just because I say I'm a failure with women. But I'm not. I'm just telling the simple truth, which is that I've never managed to give a woman satisfaction. I hope to. I hoped to with you. Given a bit of time. But in itself it's just a a perfectly neutral fact. Like the fact I was a virgin when I was with Carol. (*He breaks off for a moment*.) She was very cruel. I adored her.

CELIA: You probably adored her because she was cruel.

PHILIP: On the contrary, it was when she became really cruel that I stopped adoring her. Your interpretation is both perverse and banal.

CELIA: Oh, don't be so pompous.

PHILIP: Sorry.

CELIA: You know something, you apologize far too often. You really oughtn't to, it's not very attractive.

PHILIP: Yes, I know, I'm sorry.

(CELIA *laughs, briefly, and* PHILIP *smiles as he realizes what he has said.*)

CELIA: What made you want to get married?

PHILIP: You.

CELIA: Yes, I know, but apart from that.

PHILIP: What do you mean?

CELIA: Well, you've been a comfortable bachelor for so long, I think you must have made some kind of abstract decision to get married, I mean quite apart from wanting to marry me.

PHILIP: I suppose that might be true.

CELIA: Well, why?

PHILIP: Perhaps it was because I'm beginning to get lonely.

CELIA: Go on.

PHILIP: I don't know. I've been doing this job for about twelve or thirteen years now, and I'm beginning to realize that I'm not immortal. Another thing is, when I sit and remember the past, you know, involuntary memories, what I remember most is certain rooms, rooms I've lived and worked in, at different times, in different countries. I was thinking about some of them the other day, and I suddenly realized something that had never occurred to me before. They were all empty. I mean I remember them as if I'm sitting in them, furniture, ceiling angles, street noises, clock ticking, all very vivid. But never anyone else. It gave me rather a shock.

CELIA: Don't you like being alone?

PHILIP: No, you know how gregarious I am. Look, who's the most boring person you know?

CELIA: I don't know. If you wait a few minutes, I could probably give you quite an impressive list.

PHILIP: Well, whoever it is, I'd quite willingly spend an hour a day with him for the rest of my life. Rather than being

64

alone.

CELIA: Do you think you want to get married because you're unhappy?

PHILIP: I'm not unhappy. I mean, I am at the moment, but in general I've got no reason to be unhappy. In fact, I've got no right to be unhappy.

CELIA: That's never stopped anyone.

PHILIP: I know. I know that, but when you consider how pleasant my job is, how well-fed and privileged and comfortable I am, and how easy it is for me to be tolerant and compassionate, it does seem perverse to be unhappy as well, doesn't it? I mean, to be unhappy on top of all that does seem unreasonably self-indulgent, don't you think? It's not as if my life was a struggle. I sit in my study and read the latest journal, and occasionally I get up and change the record on my player, and sometimes I go abroad for a few weeks and wander round the galleries, and I play with words and make my anagrams and read the arts pages. And books, I must have read thousands of books, and seen hundreds of films and plays in my life. Not that many of them stay with me longer than an evening, but I'm grateful to all those people for whiling away my time. And that's all. Oh, yes, and I teach, and lecture, and write rather boring and pedantic articles, and from time to time, I suffer. Not often, I wouldn't like to exaggerate, but from time to time. A full life and an empty one.

(*He smiles.* CELIA *assesses this for a moment.*)

CELIA: Sympathy, is it, you're after?

PHILIP: Well, yes, perhaps, yes, I suppose so. I don't know. Perhaps not sympathy. Liking.

CELIA: At least you like everyone, that's half the battle anyway.

PHILIP: Yes, that's half the battle. The wrong half, but there we go.

CELIA: And you're an optimist, that makes life pleasanter, doesn't it?

PHILIP: I don't think I am. What makes you think that? You

can like people without being an optimist. For instance,
it's easier to like people if it occurs to you that they're
going to die. It's difficult not to like a man if you can
envisage his flesh falling from his bones.

CELIA: Oh dear, oh dear.

PHILIP: What?

CELIA: Let us grow amorous, you and I,
Knowing that both of us must die.

PHILIP: Who said that?

CELIA: Somebody must have.

(*Silence. Then, from the playing fields outside, a long,
mournful whistle.*)

PHILIP: Full time.

CELIA: What?

PHILIP: Nothing.

CELIA: Not being lyrical, are you?

PHILIP (*shaking his head*): I . . .

CELIA: Let us eschew lyricism. Don't you think? I think lyricism
should at all costs be eschewed.

PHILIP: Stop it.

CELIA: Well, you started it. I never realized you had a morbid
streak in you.

PHILIP (*making an effort*): Nonsense, you've always known that
I was melancholy.

CELIA: I haven't.

PHILIP: Haven't I ever told you that story about the roundabout?

CELIA: No.

PHILIP: I must have.

CELIA (*irritated*): You haven't.

PHILIP: It's by one of those French philosophers, it's meant to
be allegorical. It's an allegory of life.

CELIA: Oh, God.

PHILIP: A man drives up to this roundabout, which has three
roads leading out of it. He wants to take the first left, or
right I suppose since we're in France, but as he's about to

66

turn right, he sees there's a no entry sign. Ah, well, he says, can't be helped, we'll have to take the second right. Imagine his surprise when he sees this road has a no entry sign as well. I shall have to take the third right, he says, cursing a bit, because it's going to take him out of his way, and he's just about to turn the wheel, when he sees another no entry sign. I don't know, he says, what the bloody transport system in this country is coming to, we shall just have to go back the way we came, that's all. But lo and behold, when he goes to turn back the way he came, another no entry sign. That throws him for a bit. He carries on round the roundabout a couple of times, to make sure he hasn't made a mistake, and gradually he becomes aware of something he hasn't noticed up to now —namely that all the cars on the roundabout, which is enormous by the way, are going round and round like he is, and not one car is leaving the roundabout. Then he notices something even stranger. In the middle of the roundabout, travelling much faster than any of the cars, are three ambulances. Whizzing round and round in the centre of the roundabout. I don't know, he says, I shall have to stop, I'm feeling dizzy. But no sooner has he pulled up, than a gendarme comes over and raps on his window. "Move along, please, sir." Why, he says. "No parking. Use your head, sir, no parking on a roundabout." He sees the logic of this and wearily starts the engine up again. Then a thought strikes him, and he leans out of the window, and says, just a minute, officer, there's just one thing I'd like to ask you. "What's that, sir?" the gendarme says. Well, he says, why are those ambulances driving round at breakneck speed in the middle of the roundabout? "Oh, really, sir," the gendarme says, "don't ask silly questions, you know as well as I do ambulances have priority."
(*Silence.* CELIA *smiles weakly,* PHILIP *coughs apologetically.*)
Works better if you have a blackboard.

CELIA: Really?

PHILIP: Yes.

CELIA: And is that your view of life?

PHILIP: Well, I don't know, perhaps, I think so, yes.

CELIA: You surprise me. I didn't think you had it in you, all that gloom.

PHILIP: Oh, yes, I suppose . . . (*He pauses, before deciding to go on with what he is saying.*) All my life, you know, I've been in a state of perpetual terror.

CELIA: Terror?

PHILIP: I think that's more accurate than the word I normally use for it, which is concern.

CELIA: What do you mean?

PHILIP: I mean, I mean that the basic feature of my character is an anxiety to please people and to do what they want, which leads to, that is, which amounts to a passion, and which is, in fact, so advanced that I can only describe it as . . . terror.

CELIA: In other words, it's not that you like people, it's just that you're afraid of them.

PHILIP: No, there's no contradiction in that, the one is a consequence of the other.

CELIA: I don't believe that.

(*Silence.*)

PHILIP: Let me tell you a story I've never told anyone before, it's one of the most humiliating things that ever happened to me. When I was teaching in Hong Kong, I used to, walking from the lecture-hall to the car-park, I used to pass a hunchback, a, a cripple with an enormous head, who used to sit on the pavement and beg. After a time, I got into the habit of giving him a little money, every day, when I passed him. This went on for a bit, and then, to my great embarrassment, he started to clean my car. I tried to tell him not to bother one day when I found him at it, but he didn't understand, he just smiled and nodded and went on polishing, so I just left it, it seemed to be what he wanted

68

to do. So every day, I would come out of my lecture, walk past him, press a little money into his hand, shamefully little now I come to think of it, get into my beautiful, shiny car and drive off.

I used to keep a cache of small change handy to pay him, but one day, for some reason, I found I had none left, in fact, as I was leaving the building I found I had nothing smaller than a ten-dollar note, which was obviously, I thought to myself, far too much to give him. So, on this particular day I walked hurriedly past on the other side of street, hoping he wouldn't see me, and crossed into the car-park as quickly as I could. But I'd just got into the car and put the key in the ignition, when I saw him hobbling towards the entrance of the car-park on his crutches at great speed, stopping occasionally to wave his duster at me. No, I thought, I can't face this, so I started up, and put my foot down, and raced out of the car-park. Now, I don't know about this, I mean, I'm sure I wasn't anywhere near him, but for some reason he panicked, and tried to jump backwards—and I just had this appalling glimpse of his crutches going up in the air as he overbalanced and fell on to his back. Needless to say, I didn't stop.

After that, whenever he saw me coming, he used to get up, move down the road a bit and go indoors. I hoped I'd be able to make it up with him, but I never got a chance, he never, he never let me get near him again.

No wonder they want our blood.

CELIA: Why are you telling me all this?

PHILIP: All what?

CELIA: All these stories. I can't ever remember you talking as much as this.

PHILIP: I don't want you to go.

(*Silence.*)

CELIA: My problem is, all the men I fall in love with turn out to be such terrible people.

PHILIP: Oh. Do you think so?

CELIA: Not you, I don't mean you. That's what I'm trying to say. I was never really in love with you because you weren't firm enough. I don't think I'm capable of loving anyone as weak as you.

PHILIP: Do you prefer to be bullied then?

CELIA: I prefer to know where I stand.

(*Silence.*)

PHILIP: Can't we . . . isn't there . . . ?

CELIA: I don't think so.

PHILIP: Are you sure?

CELIA: Yes. Yes, now I've made up my mind, I honestly don't know what it is I ever saw in you.

PHILIP: Oh, well. Oh, well, then.

CELIA: No, don't misunderstand me. I'll always like you. I'll always be fond of you. It's just that we're not compatible.

PHILIP: So you already said. I still can't see it myself, but I suppose I shall just have to take your word for it.

CELIA: Now I think it would be best if I went.

(*She gets up.*)

PHILIP: Don't.

CELIA: Yes.

PHILIP: Please.

CELIA: I think it would be best.

PHILIP: Stay and talk to me. I feel a bit suicidal.

CELIA: Oh, don't exaggerate.

PHILIP: Well, you know. Stay and talk for a bit.

CELIA: Look, what have we got to talk about now? What could we possibly talk about?

PHILIP: Anything.

(CELIA *bursts into tears.* PHILIP *is amazed, he takes her in his arms and she sobs uncontrollably for a minute, then slowly recovers.*)

CELIA: Sorry.

PHILIP: Are you all right, love?

CELIA: Yes. All right now.

PHILIP: What's the matter?

70

CELIA: What do you think?

PHILIP: But I mean . . . I mean, it's your decision.

CELIA: What difference does that make?

PHILIP: All right, now, are you?

CELIA: Yes, thanks.

PHILIP: Would you like a glass of water or anything?

CELIA: No, no. I really must go now. Good-bye.

PHILIP: Good-bye. (*He takes her face in his hands and kisses her on the eyes and on the mouth.*) What now? Death, hell, destruction, suicide, or will he come through smiling?

CELIA: Yes.

PHILIP: When will I see you again?

CELIA: Not for a bit. Not until we've got over it.

PHILIP: Soon.

CELIA: I expect so. (*She moves quickly to the door.*) Good-bye. (CELIA *exits.*)

PHILIP: Good-bye, love.

(*He stands for a moment in the centre of the stage, disconsolate. Then he sits at his desk, picks up a book, and reads. He breaks off for a moment and stares into the distance, then returns to his book. He makes a note.*)

BLACKOUT

SIX

A few hours later. Evening. PHILIP *is now writing a letter, apparently with some difficulty. After a time, he puts his pen down and thinks for a moment, gazing vacantly into space.*

PHILIP: But I . . . (*He breaks off, gets up, goes over to the bookshelf, takes down a book and looks something up.*) Yes.

But I was thinking of a plan
To dye one's whiskers green,
And always use so large a fan
That they could not be seen.

Yes. (*He smiles, then, after a short pause, moves over to the telephone and dials a two-figure number.*) Hello, Don? . . . Yes . . . I wonder if you could just come round for a minute, I'd like to talk to you . . . Well, yes, it is, rather . . . it is, it's been a day of major catastrophes, and I . . . Well, in fact, I want to ask your advice about something . . . it won't take a minute, honestly . . . all right, thanks, right.

(PHILIP *crosses the room and pours himself a drink. A knock at the door and* DON *enters. He smiles at* PHILIP *and slumps into an armchair.*)

DON: Hello.

PHILIP: Scotch?

DON: Thanks.

PHILIP: Sorry to drag you over here. Are you busy?

(*He pours a drink for* DON, *takes it over to him.*)

DON: Well, no, not exactly, I . . . well, I'll tell you about it in a minute. First of all, what's your problem? You don't look very well.

PHILIP: I don't feel very well. I mean, I feel a bit remote.

DON: What do you mean?

PHILIP: Distant.

DON: Why? What's the matter?

PHILIP: Well, Celia came round this afternoon and told me she didn't want to marry me any more.

DON: Oh.

PHILIP: Last night, Araminta stayed here under circumstances too appalling to relate.

DON: Really?

PHILIP: And this morning Celia came round here before Araminta had left.

DON: Oh, I see.

PHILIP: No. Because Celia admitted that she'd decided to leave me anyway.

DON: Did she?

PHILIP: She having spent the night with Braham.

DON (*bewildered*): Good God.

PHILIP: Although she said that had nothing to do with it either.

DON: With what?

PHILIP: Her decision.

(*Silence.*)

DON: How extraordinary.

PHILIP: She said what you said when we were talking about it yesterday. She said she didn't think we were compatible.

DON: Meaningless nonsense.

PHILIP: But you said that as well.

DON: Yes. But I was speaking theoretically.

PHILIP (*uncomprehending*): Oh.

DON: You see, I always divide people into two groups. Those who live by what they know to be a lie, and those who live by what they believe, falsely, to be the truth. And having decided that Celia belonged to the first group and you to the second, I concluded that you weren't compatible, and that furthermore that was what attracted you to one another. But, I mean, trying to make elegant patterns out of people's hopelessness doesn't really work. It's only a frivolous game.

PHILIP: Seems to have worked on this occasion.

DON: What is wrong with the statement: "all generalizations are false"?

PHILIP: It's a generalization.

DON: See, you're not as remote as all that.

PHILIP: But why . . . why do you say I live by what I believe, falsely, to be the truth?

DON: Because you do. Your whole behaviour is based on the assumption that everyone is like you.

PHILIP: Isn't everybody's?

DON: No. Of course not. Most people's behaviour is based on desperate hope that everyone isn't like them.

PHILIP: And why do you think Celia lives by a lie?

DON: Because her vanity demands it.

PHILIP: I'm not sure about that.

DON: I am.

PHILIP: Well, no doubt if you go on about it long enough, you'll persuade me to believe it. I haven't even got the courage of my lack of convictions.

DON: Oh, I wish I'd said that.

PHILIP: Why?

DON: I don't know, it sounds good.

PHILIP: That's not really why I said it, believe it or not.

DON: Sorry. I'm sorry.

(*Silence.*)

PHILIP: And which category do you belong to?

DON: What?

PHILIP: Of the two.

DON: Oh, I live by a lie. In my case, the lie is that I am a teacher of English, when in fact I am paid a handsome sum by the college to perfect a technique of idleness which I hope will eventually become unparalleled in academic

74

history.

PHILIP: Oh, rubbish, you're not idle. You're famous for your conscientiousness.

DON: Ah, well, that's part of the art. I perform, in fact I sometimes actually volunteer for, all those little administrative tasks, which require no effort or application whatsoever and which can be done quite automatically. In that way, you see, I acquire a reputation for conscientiousness, and also provide myself with an excuse in the unlikely event that I should be caught out not knowing something I ought to know.

PHILIP: You're exaggerating.

DON: Oh, no, I'm not. In my youth I might have been concerned about my idleness, I used to make feeble attacks on it by doing things like setting my striking clock an hour fast, but I think I knew all along what I was heading for. When I struggled through my finals in that cunning and devious way, I think I knew this was my destination. I worked hard my first year teaching, my God, yes. I took a couple of dozen index cards and noted down ten points about each of the subjects that might reasonably be expected to come my way. And now, twenty-four weeks a year, I simply select the relevant card and give my pupils the points they omitted in their essays, or if they've got them all I say, wonderful, see you next week, and I recover from this strenuous activity with twenty-eight weeks a year of total inactivity, usually in some pleasantly warm climate. I've given up all ideas of writing books, research, all that nonsense, I'm just settling, settling into my character. I am more than half in love with easeful sloth. I'm . . . what's that word that means bloodless?

PHILIP: Etiolated?

DON: Etiolated. That's it, etiolated. Only fit for lying about on a sofa with the curtains pulled, listening to baroque music. and occasionally dabbing at the temples with a damp flannel. Do you know that I'm capable now of emptying my head completely for two or three hours at a stretch? Not a single thought of any kind. Nothing. That's not easily done, you know.

PHILIP: I'm sure.

DON: I think that if one manages in one's lifetime not only to come to terms with one's own uselessness but to begin actually enjoying it as well, that's something, don't you think, something, some kind of . . . an achievement.

PHILIP: Perhaps.

(*Silence.*)

DON: I'm sorry, Philip.

PHILIP: Why?

DON: It's typical of you, you know.

PHILIP: What?

DON: You've had the most terrible day, everything has gone wrong, you ask me round to give you some support or advice or something and all that happens is that I talk about myself.

PHILIP: That's all right.

DON: I'll shut up now. You tell me what you want. What can I do for you?

PHILIP: Well, when I was talking to Celia this afternoon, she asked me why I wanted to get married, I mean, apart from wanting to marry her. It made me realize that she was right, that I did want to get married, that I was lonely, now that youthful hopes have faded in the usual way, that it wasn't only her. It's all right when you're with people, when there's someone there, as long as there are people there to fill the air with plausible sounds. It's when the silence comes . . . you know, I find it whistles and rings now, the older I am, the louder it seems to get, the silence. I'm sorry, I didn't mean to get maudlin.

DON: No, go on. What is friendship, if not a chance to indulge in mutual self-pity?

PHILIP: And I was thinking what you said to me yesterday about Liz.

DON (*shiftily*): Oh?

PHILIP: Yes, you remember you were saying you thought she liked me, and that she would be more suitable for me than Celia.

DON: Well. . . .

PHILIP: Anyway, I've just sat down to write to her, I thought I'd ask her out or something, ask her to lunch, and I just wanted to ask you what. . . . (*He breaks off, surprised by* DON's *obvious embarrassment.*) What's the matter?

DON: Well, Liz is, she's in my room now.

PHILIP: Is she?

DON: She's been there since yesterday evening.

PHILIP: Oh. Oh, that's . . . erm . . .

DON: So I . . .

PHILIP: Yes. Yes.

DON: I've rather, you know, rather fallen for her.

PHILIP: Oh, well, that's, er, isn't it?

DON: Yes.

PHILIP: I'm surprised, I didn't think you . . .

DON: I'm surprised, too, in fact, I'm amazed. She's such a quiet girl, I mean, you don't expect her to be, I mean, it just sort of happened, and then for her to be, well, so passionate, I was very surprised.

PHILIP: Yes.

DON: I'm sorry, Philip, it's just the way things happen. . . .

PHILIP: That's all right.

DON: The last thing . . .

PHILIP: That's all right. Perhaps you should be going back now.

DON: No, it's all right.

PHILIP: I'd rather you did.

DON: No, look, you're just a bit upset . . .

PHILIP: Will you please get out!

DON: Oh, all right, if you . . .

PHILIP: Please go away!

(DON *exits uncertainly.* PHILIP *sits for a moment. Then he drains his drink, gets up, moves to his desk, crumples up the*

77

letter and throws it into the waste-paper basket. Next he moves back to the table, takes a cigarette from the cigarette-box and puts it in his mouth. Pause. Then he returns to the desk, opens a drawer and takes out a small pistol. He considers it for a moment, then puts it down on the desk. He lifts the telephone and dials two figures.)

Hello, Don? . . . I'm sorry about all that . . . yes, I just, you know, well, I am sorry anyway. . . . What? . . . Now? All right, if you're sure that's all right . . . are you sure? . . . Yes, I am quite hungry . . . well, that's very kind . . . yes, I'm all right, now . . . no, don't let's get sentimental about it . . . well, anyway, I'm about to do something terrible . . . you'll see in a minute. . . . I forgot to tell you, I thought of a new anagram today . . . "imagine the theatre as real" . . . "imagine the theatre as real" . . . it's an anagram for "I hate thee, sterile anagram". . . . Yes, I thought so too . . . all right, then . . . yes . . . yes . . . see you both in a minute.

(*He hangs up, pauses a moment, then picks up the pistol. He turns it toward him and pulls the trigger. A small flame springs from the hammer.* PHILIP *lights his cigarette from it, inhales deeply, pockets the pistol and leaves the stage.*)

(*Aria: "Ich freue mich auf meinen Tod" from Bach's Cantata No. 82, "Ich habe genug".*)

CURTAIN

re

THE PHILANTHROPIST

by the same author

*

WHEN DID YOU LAST SEE MY MOTHER?
TOTAL ECLIPSE